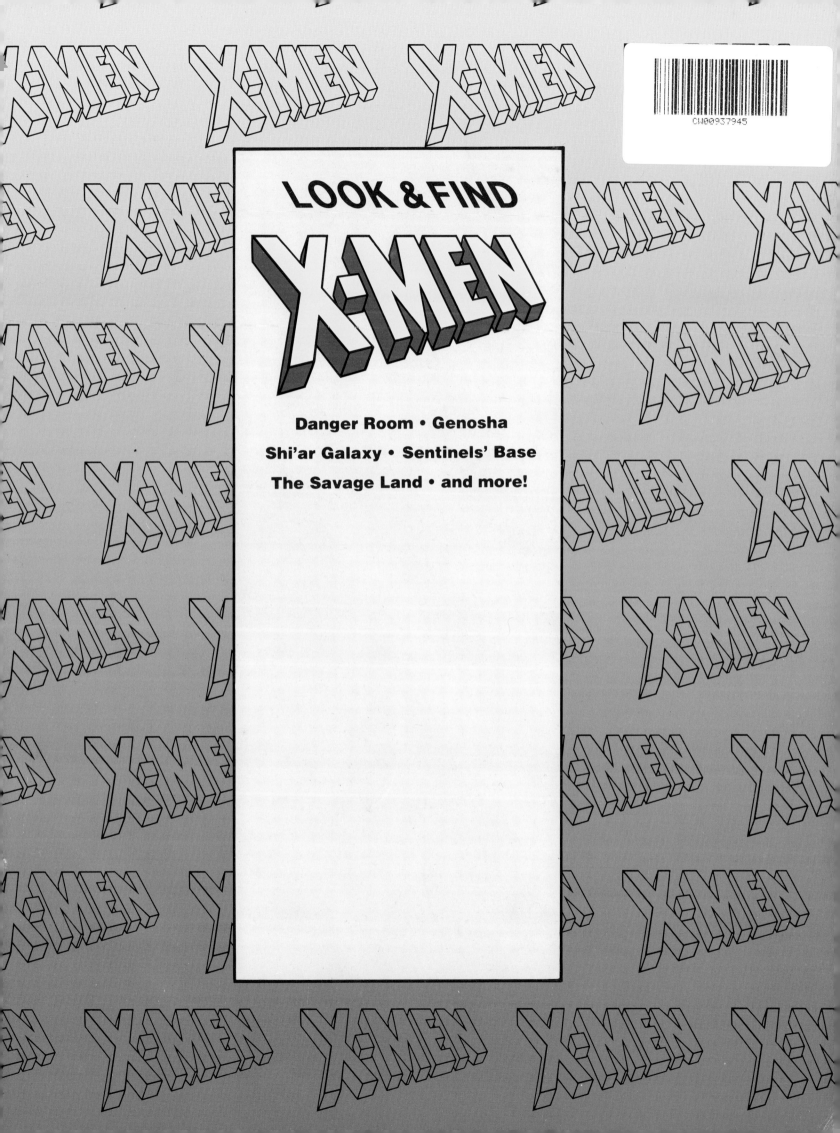

LOOK & FIND

X-MEN

Danger Room • Genosha

Shi'ar Galaxy • Sentinels' Base

The Savage Land • and more!

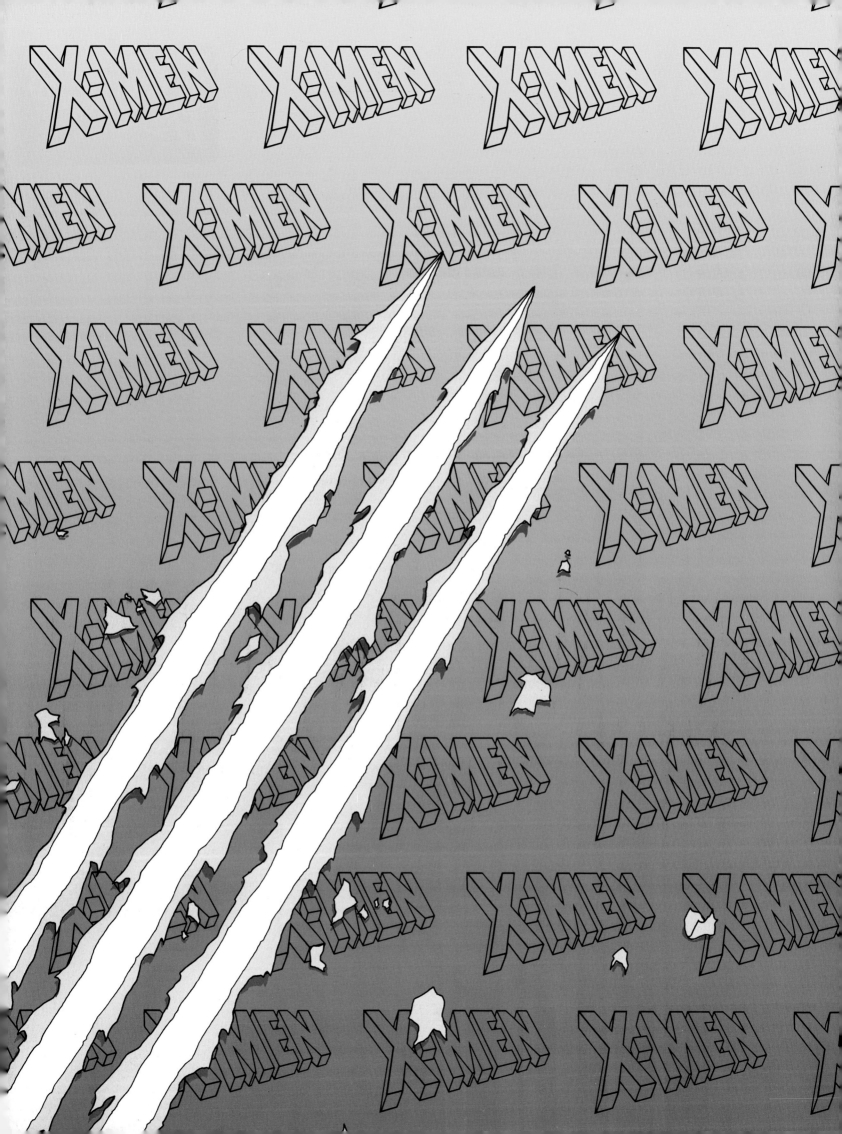

LOOK & FIND

X·MEN

Danger Room • Genosha

Shi'ar Galaxy • Sentinels' Base

The Savage Land • and more!

Illustrator/Illustration Coordinator: James Janes
Inker: Dave Simons
Colorists: Janice Parker; Michele Marrero-DeCicco

Illustration Script Development by Dwight Zimmerman

First published in Great Britain in 1994 by Boxtree Limited,
Broadwall House, 21 Broadwall, London SE1 9PL

10 9 8 7 6 5 4 3 2 1

ISBN: 1-85283-389-0

Printed and bound in Italy

A CIP catalogue entry for this book is available from the
British Library

B⊞XTREE

I'VE NEVER SEEN SUCH CHAOS IN THE DANGER ROOM. FIRST MAGNETO BURST IN WITH HIS MINDMASTER DEVICE, PLANNING TO ENSLAVE THE X-MEN! JUST WHEN IT SEEMED HE MIGHT SUCCEED, GATEWAY APPEARED AND USED HIS MUTANT ABILITIES TO CREATE A TORNADO THAT FRAGMENTED THE MIND-MASTER DEVICE AND DIS-RUPTED THE FABRIC OF TIME! I SENSE THAT GATEWAY'S INTENTIONS ARE GOOD, BUT I STILL DON'T SEE WHAT HE HAS IN MIND.

HELP PROFESSOR XAVIER AND THE X-MEN MAKE SENSE OF THIS CONFUSION. BEGIN BY FINDING THE PIECES OF MAGNETO'S MINDMASTER DEVICE,

RADAR DISH
CONTROL PANEL
MAIN HOUSING UNIT
GYROSCOPE
TRIPOD
RADAR SCREEN

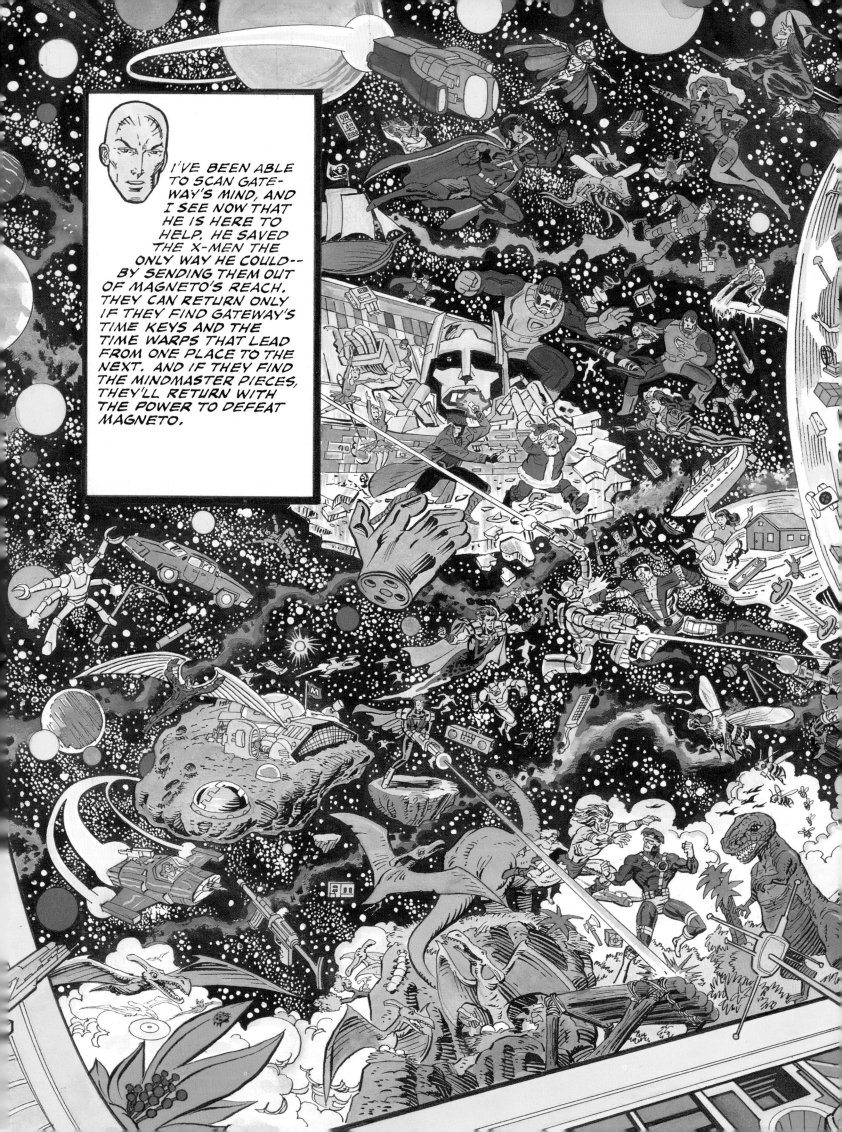

BRAVE THE DANGERS OF THE SAVAGE LAND AND FIND THESE ITEMS FOR THE X-MEN.

GENOSHAN RIFLE

NO MUTANTS SIGN

GYROSCOPE

GATEWAY'S TIME WARP

GENOSHAN HELMET

PIPELINE

SEE IF YOU CAN SPOT THE ITEMS THE X-MEN NEED TO TAKE THE NEXT STEP IN THEIR BATTLE WITH MAGNETO.

MAGNETO'S FLAG

ACOLYTE'S HELMET

SINGLE SEAT ROCKET PLANE

FABIAN CORTEZ

RADAR DISH

GATE-WAY'S TIME WARP

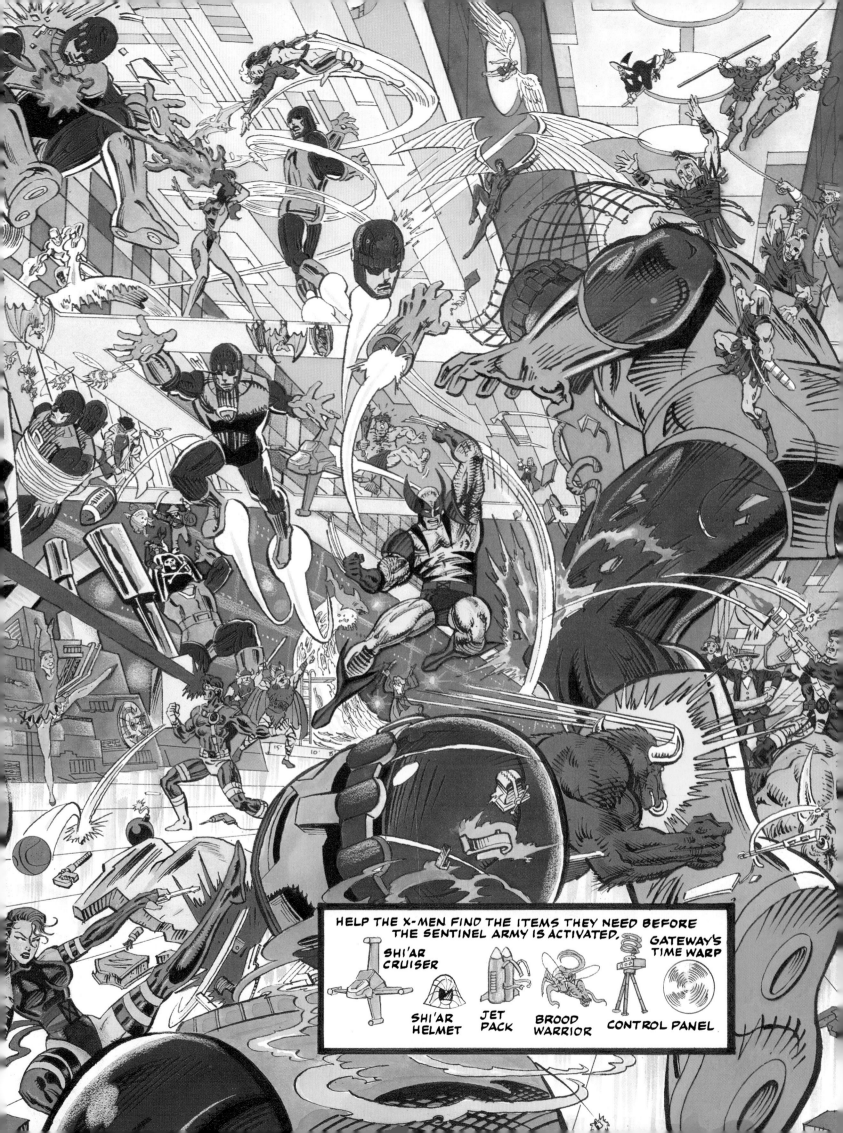

MY FAVORITE LITTLE VACATION SPOT--THE SHI'AR GALAXY. YOU CAN ALWAYS FIND A GOOD FIGHT HERE, AND TODAY'S NO EXCEPTION. THE BROOD'S AT IT AGAIN, AND PRINCESS LILANDRA AND HER WARRIORS COULD USE OUR HELP. I DON'T MIND TAKIN' OUT A FEW SLEAZOIDS WHILE WE LOOK FOR GATEWAY'S TIME KEYS.

THE X-MEN NEED THE FOLLOWING ITEMS TO MOVE ON FROM HERE. SEE IF YOU CAN HELP FIND THEM.

ROBOT JANITOR

ROBOT GUARD

ROBOT WAITER

POTTED PLANT

MAIN HOUSING UNIT

GATEWAY'S TIME WARP

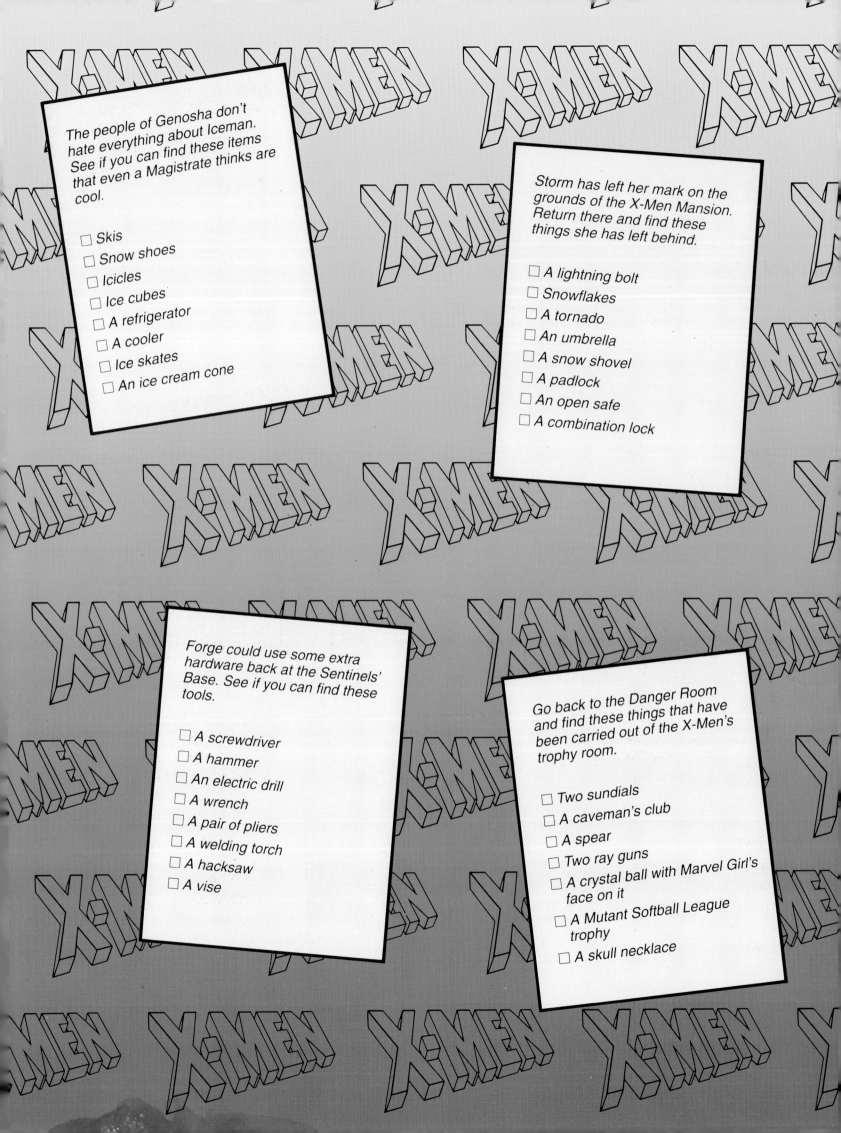

The people of Genosha don't hate everything about Iceman. See if you can find these items that even a Magistrate thinks are cool.

- ☐ Skis
- ☐ Snow shoes
- ☐ Icicles
- ☐ Ice cubes
- ☐ A refrigerator
- ☐ A cooler
- ☐ Ice skates
- ☐ An ice cream cone

Storm has left her mark on the grounds of the X-Men Mansion. Return there and find these things she has left behind.

- ☐ A lightning bolt
- ☐ Snowflakes
- ☐ A tornado
- ☐ An umbrella
- ☐ A snow shovel
- ☐ A padlock
- ☐ An open safe
- ☐ A combination lock

Forge could use some extra hardware back at the Sentinels' Base. See if you can find these tools.

- ☐ A screwdriver
- ☐ A hammer
- ☐ An electric drill
- ☐ A wrench
- ☐ A pair of pliers
- ☐ A welding torch
- ☐ A hacksaw
- ☐ A vise

Go back to the Danger Room and find these things that have been carried out of the X-Men's trophy room.

- ☐ Two sundials
- ☐ A caveman's club
- ☐ A spear
- ☐ Two ray guns
- ☐ A crystal ball with Marvel Girl's face on it
- ☐ A Mutant Softball League trophy
- ☐ A skull necklace

In the fury of the battle, Lilandra, Majestrix of the Shi'ar Empire, has lost some personal belongings. See if you can help her locate them.

☐ Her throne
☐ Her scepter
☐ Her crown
☐ Her royal robe
☐ Her signet ring
☐ Her imperial staff
☐ Her royal necklace

Cerebro requires a lot of spare parts. Go back to the Cerebro Room and look for these extra computer components.

☐ A floppy disk
☐ A printer
☐ A monitor
☐ A keyboard
☐ A circuit board
☐ A mouse
☐ A laser disk

Return to the Savage Land and find these things that might make you think of Cyclops.

☐ A monocle
☐ An eye patch
☐ A pair of sunglasses
☐ A red ruby
☐ A mythological Cyclops
☐ An eye chart
☐ A one-eyed jack

Gambit is an expert at games. Go back to Asteroid M and find these objects he uses to compete in his favorite activities.

☐ A basketball
☐ A baseball
☐ A chess king
☐ A dart board
☐ A soccer ball
☐ A football
☐ A volleyball
☐ A pair of dice

Jubilee has left some stuff scattered around the Mall. Go back and help her track down these missing items.

☐ Sunglasses
☐ A comb
☐ A purse
☐ A boom box
☐ Headphones
☐ A skateboard
☐ A reading lamp

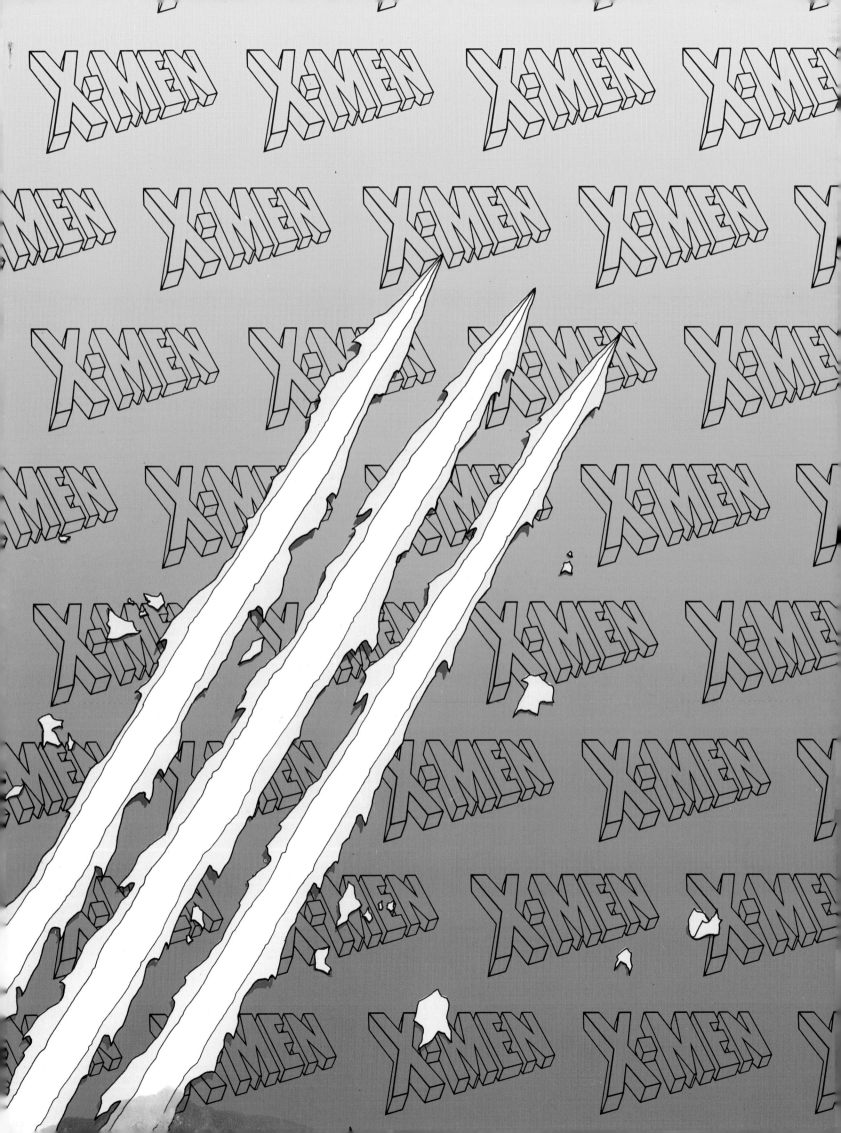